2022

RHYMECRAFT

Edited By Sarah Waterhouse

First published in Great Britain in 2022 by:

Young Writers
Remus House
Coltsfoot Drive
Peterborough
PE2 9BF
Telephone: 01733 890066
Website: www.youngwriters.co.uk

Printed and bound in the UK by BookPrintingUK
Website: www.bookprintinguk.com
YB0509Y

FOREWORD

For Young Writers' latest competition This Is Me,
we asked primary school pupils to look inside
themselves, to think about what makes them unique,
and then write a poem about it! They rose to the
challenge magnificently and the result is this fantastic
collection of poems in a variety of poetic styles.

Here at Young Writers our aim is to encourage creativity
in children and to inspire a love of the written word, so
it's great to get such an amazing response, with some
absolutely fantastic poems. It's important for children to
focus on and celebrate themselves and this competition
allowed them to write freely and honestly, celebrating
what makes them great, expressing their hopes and
fears, or simply writing about their favourite things.
This Is Me gave them the power of words. The result
is a collection of inspirational and moving poems that
also showcase their creativity and writing ability.

I'd like to congratulate all the young poets
in this anthology, I hope this inspires them
to continue with their creative writing.

CONTENTS

Independent Entries

Ronav Gavirneni (9)   1
Liv Coates (11)   2
Ava Gilbert (11)   6
Alice Tyler (9)   9
Saif Ahmed (9)   10
Natalie Ritchie (9)   13
Hanna Zhang (10)   14
Anya Lester (9)   16
Dhruva Rao (10)   18
James Butler (9)   20
Olutowo Omotoso (8)   22
Eva Sloan (10)   24
Thomas Mathieson   26
Isabella Searle (9)   29
Nysa Valentine (9)   30
Jemimah Rashid (11)   32
Vihaan George (10)   34
Isla Scott (12)   36
Thomas Butler (10)   38
Lucas Liu (8)   40
Bram Thompson (9)   42
Lydia Gebrihiwot (9)   44
Kweli Baillie (10)   46
Thomas J Noon   48
Madeline Roberts (11)   50
Daisy Clarke (8)   52
Malavika Nair (10)   54
Dua E Zainab (11)   56
Tate Hassall (11)   58
Aadya Arya (11)   60
Rosanna Ren (9)   62
Maya Oxborrow (9)   64
Zaynah Jabeen-Iqbal (7)   66
Ayza Hanif (10)   68

Idris Jones (9)   70
Aaditri Manjunath (8)   72
Alara Logie (8)   74
Ishaq Munir   76
Libby Lethbridge (9)   78
Archit Shenoy (11)   80
Orla Salmon (8)   82
Fausta Kiselyte (11)   84
Parth Aggarwal (10)   86
Aakriti Barpanda (10)   87
Katie Thornton (9)   88
Jacey May Gardiner (10)   90
Olivia O'Neill (9)   92
Harris Katiisa Cheney (9)   93
Myah Jones (9)   94
Mary Willan (11)   95
Aadharshya Maran (9)   96
Poppy Picton (9)   98
Aaina Chopra (11)   99
Naomi Matthews (11)   100
Zoha Mehdi (9)   101
Abiwaran Parameswaran (11)   102
Griffith-Nmaju (9)   103
Darcey Hassett (8)   104
Virat Manchambatla (7)   106
Emily Norton (8)   107
Chaplin (9)   108
Audrey Laurent (10)   109
Isabel Greenwood (8)   110
Elinor Keller (8)   112
Arun Darar (10)   113
Ola Ukoha (10)   114
Nia Vale (9)   115
Eva Langridge (9)   116
Anna Donovan (10)   117

Musa Muhammad (8)	118	Amy Freeman (8)	164
Esmay Steward (11)	119	Theo Calafatis (8)	165
Fatima Mahmood (8)	120	Fiona Olubori (10)	166
Scarlett Little-Kerr	122	Isla Aharon (8)	167
Warizah Fatma	124	Henry Gee (8)	168
Selma Abdullah (9)	125	Jedelyn Campos Aragon	169
Neev Kaur-Chakravarti (8)	126	Sasha McGlynn	170
Akshath Bandreddi (9)	127	Joanna Luncan (11)	171
Aarav Chakraverty (10)	128	Radhika Satish	172
Sehansa De Silva (9)	129	Zahra Anis (10)	173
Kunarathan Parameswaran (9)	130	Islah Malik (10)	174
Lexie-Jae Lomax (10)	131	Laraib Malik (11)	176
Evie Sadler (11)	132	Jesziah Atan	177
Felicity Rogers (9)	133	Noah Flavelle (10)	178
Charlotte Ruby Karger (11)	134	Maiya Sandberg (7)	179
Kwame Baillie (8)	135	Maple Doherty (14)	180
Lara Almashta (10)	136	Elizabeth Edwards (7)	181
Azalea Ward (8)	138	Amenaghawon Olaye (9)	182
Abhay Khanna (9)	139	Thomas Keenan (7)	183
Daisy-Mae Gaunt (10)	140	Madison Ward (10)	184
Andrea Fuorvito (7)	141	Samson Cohen (7)	185
Pavaki Singh (8)	142	Jasmine Patel (7)	186
Elizabeth Wamalwa (12)	143	Daphne Erkut (8)	187
Aarya Dubey (7)	144	Anamta Abrar (9)	188
Edward Farr (9)	145	Oma Olaye (11)	189
Harijeeth Reddy Parvatha	146	Abigail Miller (9)	190
Sienna Scarff (8)	147	Nathaniel Rose (9)	191
Evie Corcoran (11)	148	Anna Legg (7)	192
Amaeya Iyengar (7)	149	Isabelle Freya George (10)	193
Katelyn Stone (9)	150	Laura Figoli (8)	194
Aadam Hussain (3)	151	Skylar Mansell	195
Isabelle Robinson (10)	152	Lola Crossley (10)	196
Saswath Govindasamy Raja (7)	153	Ashvika Shenoy (8)	197
Poppy Halsall (11)	154	Nabeeha Khandaker (10)	198
Greta Winkelgrund (10)	156	Sara Figoli (8)	199
Miley Colbourne (7)	157	Nancy Harris (8)	200
Corey Wilton (10)	158	Mason Wright (10)	201
Muhammad Ayaan	159	Alishba Latif (11)	202
Mehmood (9)		Indie Dawber (8)	203
Laila Gregory	160	Isobel Crowther (10)	204
Vishnusri Priya Mendu (11)	161	Madison Reddaway (8)	205
Josiah Campbell (10)	162	Seren Campbell (9)	206
Emilia Salter (9)	163	Avi Patel (9)	207

Harmony Tendo (9)	208
Sophie Wilson	209
Georgi	210
Syeda Hamnah Shah (10)	211
Oliver Tabita (10)	212
Thomas Manns-Moran	213
Jenna Islam (8)	214
Ziad Abdelnaby (9)	215
Alveen Muhammad	216
Shreya Bhardwaj (11)	217
Nanaki Sandhu (9)	218
Harley Haldane (9)	219
Ophelia Morgan-Dew (7)	220
Harley Vahabzadeh (8)	221
Alexandra Dankowska (9)	222
Sukeeth Venkiteela (7)	223
Ólan Tracey	224
Chloe Thorley (8)	225
Teddy Mitchel (7)	226
Dillon Smith (11)	227
Maya Leeming (9)	228
Devna Sanal	229
Jessica Manns-Moran	230
Mahder Yohanes	231
Edwyn Rhys-Davies (7)	232

THE POEMS

This Is Me!

R iding on a train is an epic journey,

O micron is such a jerk,

N ervously looking out for people who are coughing,

A nd do you know that they might have COVID?

V isiting lots of places is not a good choice when you know it's lockdown,

G alloping through the country, you will find luck because who knows? Someone kind might get you a perfect medicine,

A cross the country there have been rising COVID cases,

V iruses have been roaming the Earth for millions of years,

I t's really terrifying,

R eally, as if there is a bloodthirsty vampire haunting the world,

N ever-ending viruses are really bad for the Earth,

E very single day, try to be as hygienic as you can,

N ew variants in the news have been terrifying me!

I t's haunting me!

Ronav Gavirneni (9)

The Worry Monsters

Do you ever feel like you're so exhausted and you just can't be bothered?
That's the work of a worry monster.
It starts off small, rooting itself in your mind.
Then, as it grows, it absorbs your energy.
Like a bloodthirsty vampire draining the life from its victim,
Until you curl up into a ball of endless nothingness.

Wait. Just breathe.
I will not let my worries control me.
I will not let my anxiety break me.
I will open up and tell someone.
I will simply breathe.

Do you ever feel like the world is on your shoulders and you just can't take it?
That's the work of a worry monster.
It starts off as a single creature perched on your shoulder.
But before you can do anything, it's not alone anymore,

Like the infectious cells in a virus, it spreads and multiplies,
Until you collapse under the heavy burden.

Wait. Just breathe.
I will not let my worries control me.
I will not let my anxiety break me.
I will open up and tell someone.
I will simply breathe.

Do you ever feel like you're shaking badly and you just can't focus?
That's the work of a worry monster.
It starts off as a shadow in the darkest corners of your thoughts.
Lurking ready to pounce when you least expect it,
Like a torturous bright light flashing to an unknown disorder,
Until you are a trembling, nervous, fidgety wreck.

Wait. Just breathe.
I will not let my worries control me.
I will not let my anxiety break me.

I will open up and tell someone.
I will simply breathe.

Do you ever feel like you're being smothered and you just can't breathe?
That's the work of a worry monster.
It starts off welcoming and safe - a comforting blanket around your shoulders,
But bit by bit, it tightens its hold, slowly suffocating you,
Like a treacherous snake constricting its defenceless prey,
Until your chest cries out, helplessly in agony.

Wait. Just breathe.
I will not let my worries control me.
I will not let my anxiety break me.
I will open up and tell someone.
I will simply breathe.

Do you ever feel like you're completely alone and you just can't cope anymore?
That's the work of a worry monster.
It starts off a murky blur of uncertainty, distorting the world around you.

Growing and growing, it becomes a dreary dense
darkness,
Like thunderous storm clouds choking the once
clear skies,
Until you get lost in the hopeless, incessant gloom.

Wait. Just breathe.
I will not let my worries control me.
I will not let my anxiety break me.
I will open up and tell someone.
I will simply breathe.

Liv Coates (11)

This Is Me

I'm not different, nothing special or smart
I'm not an angel but afraid to be a devil.
I don't tell tales but never get into trouble
I'm not a teacher's pet but neither a rebel.
I haven't figured myself out,
I'm still not sure who I was destined to be.
Where others burn, I melt -
Different but unseen.
I don't get a say in my life
But instead give others control before it is taken
forcibly.
My father often said, "Your life is a ship.
Brave the storms and cut through the waves,"
But I cower below.
The wheel is waiting,
I just need to take hold.
I'm a normal girl, brown hair, brown eyes.
It's easy to blend into the crowd.
I've never been bullied or left alone,
But then again, I've never gotten too close.
You see, I listen when others speak,

And I think while others play.
I'm that person at the back of the picture.
The one you turn to when there's no one left.
The backup in case your friend doesn't show.
I don't mind; at least I'm liked.
There's only one trait they really value though -
Something that keeps me in the mix.
I listen.
When two friends fall out, I hear their pain,
I comfort their tears and accept their burden.
Everyone thinks the listeners are quiet
But inside my opinions, my words, churn;
So, I bottle them up and listen.
I was never meant to shine like a star,
To sing in the limelight.
Everyone wants to be famous:
A reporter, an actor, a singer, an author...
But all I want is to be heard.
No one ever wonders how I get rid of my worries.
I don't tell -
That's not what I do, I'm a listener.
Instead, I bleed my troubles onto paper.

Because paper doesn't judge.
Paper always understands.
Listeners don't just have ears -
Most people forget they have mouths as well.
It's time for me to smash the bottle,
To grab hold of the wheel and never let it go,
Because I'm not just here for everyone else -
I'm here for myself and maybe it's time I stopped
being so quiet and started living.
Because I want everyone to see the real me.

Ava Gilbert (11)

This Is Me

I have two cuddly cute cats
They love to chase mice and rats
I'm sometimes brave, sometimes shy
I'm sometimes joyful but sometimes I cry

I love to dance, jump and sing
And my favourite seasons are winter and spring
My dad's from England and my mum's from
Mauritius
And I think my mum's chocolate cake is so
nutritious
I have an older brother who likes to read and
game
Even though we get on as siblings, we aren't quite
the same

I love to cook and bake
And my favourite, of course, is chocolate cake
What I love most is to write all the time
Stories, comics and poems that rhyme
So that's why I'm writing for you to see
This rhyming poem all about me!

Alice Tyler (9)

Our Bustling City

In this, our city, I have a kitty,
And he is like the Flash.
He doesn't crash, he doesn't bash,
He runs smoothly, like the Flash.

He has a laser toy that shoots a red dot,
He dashes, he dashes, he dashes at the dot.

After he plays, he eats from his red pot.
And on our sofa, he has his own spot.

In this, our city, I have my family, but that's not
including my cute cat,
I have one sibling, a mum and a dad.
There's my older sister, who can really be a blister,
and she is twenty-one.
My mum is forty-three and my dad is forty-five.
Forty-five!
That's almost the age of my gran.

My gran is above sixty and she doesn't use a fan.
She only uses a heater, and she's the opposite of a
cheetah!

In this, our city, it's not a pity because it's pretty large.
It does get crowded on the train sometimes, but you really don't need to barge!

And if you're craving a pizza,
There are pizza places and grocery shops where both the veggies and the meats are.
And then you can drive it back in a car.
You can pop to the shops to buy a jar,
Then fill it up with chocolate bars!

In this, our city, our buses are red, our roads are grey and our currency is pounds.
In this, our bustling large city, we have so many different sounds:
Like sirens wailing and boats speedily sailing,
Along this, our River Thames.

In this, our bustling city,
Things just are so pretty.
We live right here, in London town,
Where sometimes people smile and sometimes people frown.

Chicken and chips for dinner,
And even if I lose (although I'll feel a bruise),
I'll still feel like I'm a winner!

Maybe for tonight though I should just have a
chicken wrap,
And, in a little while, I'll hear you all clap,
Because this is the end of my rap.
So... mind the gap!

And that's a wrap!

Saif Ahmed (9)

Happier Than Ever

To my dear friend Maya

Hi
I don't know you, but I hope you're nice
You probably are, but I always think twice
I'm not that smart, but I'm always learning
And hopefully doing a little earning
I've got some great friends, five in particular
They're smart, funny, kind and so organised
Which is useful because I'm about as organised as
the inside of a ball of wool
I love birds and animals and will always sit
And listen and even communicate a bit
I'll read a book when I'm feeling sad
It'll always help me to not feel so bad
I'm as sneaky as a cat
And as good at telling lies as a...
Let's just say as good at telling lies as something
that's not particularly good at telling lies
But things are great
And I'm happier than ever.

Natalie Ritchie (9)

My Big Move

I lived in London, I studied hard
At a great girls' school - so academic!
Then everything changed as times transformed
My life turned round by the new pandemic

I sowed my hopes deep down
Normality will come back around

I had to move to China - quick and fast!
Hotel quarantine lasted months but passed
I adopted a pup - he was my delight
Beat COVID frights - I wore masks day and night

The grass was green, the sky was blue
It all seemed the same - yet so different too
Cold weather, new culture... so much adjustment
All seemed fine - but was I content?

I sowed my hopes deep down
Normality will come back around

A tiring day at school, much longer than before
Always revising tests behind the door

Not much creativity - lack of breadth
I entered Young Writers and found my strength

Tackling maths was no more a bone to chew
Gained confidence - a warrior's heart to rule
I won nine awards - none were easy
I learnt to be a model and went on TV!

I sowed my hopes deep down
Normality will come back around

I'm a cross-continental student - it's so cool!
Virtual lessons saved my English - and my Chinese
too
There were several bitter memories, shedding tears
There were sweeter ones too, shared with friends
these past years

COVID was a curse, threatening life and freedom
It was hard not to be beaten by this phantom
Learning was a challenge but I managed and I
made it
By holding onto hope, I survived and thrived and
nailed it.

Hanna Zhang (10)

Who Am I?

My smooth eyes fluttered shut as I lay upon my
bed,
Carried by my dreams, I woke in this world instead.
A forest full of magic and excitement all around,
A strange clock is ticking, and it's getting rather
loud.

I spy upon a mirror and expect to see my face,
But then I don't see me and all my hope escapes.
Who am I, what is happening, what is going on?
The clock ticks even louder, and the magic's all but
gone.

"Grow up," roared a bear. "You've got to be
mature...
Forget your foolish habits and close the childhood
door!"
A growing fear and pain struck through my
beating heart,
I was not expecting this, especially this part.

"Don't listen!" said a squirrel playing merrily,
"He forgets about the fun that life must surely be."

There was a sudden silence and my mind was so confused,
Is there someone who can help me deal with all this news?

I realised I've grown up and the child in me is gone!
These two sides are fighting and it's going on and on.
The time has really flown and I wish I could go back,
How I long to be so small and watch my Crackerjack.

I am sitting in my bed, the dream time must be up,
Thank heavens I'm a child and still drinking from a cup!
I am still kind and loving, and acting very happy
But sometimes I get angry and often look quite scrappy.

Anya Lester (9)

This Is Me

This is me; all joyful and free.
I'm empathetic, honest and kind;
With a rather clever mind!
I'm brave, adventurous and daring
I'm also very caring.
I am a fiery red ball;
That is constantly blaring.
I am full of happiness and fun -
But can also get angry and be a stun.
When I'm feeling upset or sad -
I always go to my mum and dad.
I'm full of elation,
With a few spots of frustration.
I am respectful and fair, and take a lot of care,
In everything I do, like this poem for me and you.
I'm also funny and I like to make people laugh;
Soon they'll be rolling around in the grass.
I'm active and brave like a lion;
But calm as a free bird flying.
I love cricket and I like to read
I'm someone who helps others in need;

And takes the lead.
I like drawing, Rubik's cube and chess
In which I impress, but need to progress,
And soon I'll be full of success.
I like maths, sports and guitar
I'm a shiny shooting star!
I enjoy tennis and football
In football, I'm a defender, I tackle all.
My favourite lessons are maths and PE,
I like how you can run around and be free.
I've got black hair, olive skin,
Brown eyes that are sparkling!
I am kind and I've got lots of friends
Now sadly, my poem has come to an end.

Dhruva Rao (10)

Monopoly

Buying houses, I have even more than Dad!
Cash floating all around me, I catch it in my hands.
My face is beaming, Mum calls me 'Mister Moneybags',
And she smiles and touches my arm.
I give her a hundred dollars and tell her, "For being so beautiful."
Jail, oh no, how have I landed here? I followed all the rules! I'm a good kid, Mama said!
The two dice roll from my hands, with a shake for good luck...
I count the four and the two they've landed on. I rolled a six! Freedom!
My little red houses can go back to collecting rent.
My Thor, God of Thunder, milkshake is almost on the last bit of ice cream,
Dad looks and says it's time to cash in.
Addition signs jumping around above my head,
I count and count and count some more, I'm the winner!
I am a winner. This is me!
A photograph with Harley Quinn, she was cardboard, but I didn't care.

No one else got to strike a pose.
Mum ruffled my hair and told me the winner got to choose a new dice,
And with her eyes gestured towards a shelf of glass jars filled with a million colourful squares.
I see mine immediately, it's gold and full of glitter and good luck, just like me.
It's perfect.
The day is perfect.
This is me!

James Butler (9)

Me!

My life is quite simple
I might have tiny pimples
But I am who I am
My name might be Sam
And I might like jam

I might be bold and sporty
Or I might be timid and lazy
But I know who I am
I might just live on the farm
And I might move in a pram

I might be funny
My nose might be runny
But I know how I smell
I might know how to spell
And I might collect seashells

I might like Captain America
My friend might be called Erica
But I know who I like
I might like to go on hikes
And I might have gone to Scafell Pike

I might be adventurous
My hikes might be dangerous
But I know what I'm scared of
I might be as graceful as a dove
And I might have had my own stove

I might be a headteacher
My brain might be a different creature
But I know what I am
I might be 0.5 kilograms
And I might like to work out anagrams

I am
Olutowo
Funny, cheerful
Daughter of Tola and Fola
Sister of Olutomi
Likes reading books and going outside
Feels happy when eating
Creative, unique
Omotoso.

Olutowo Omotoso (8)

I Am Me

I am me.
I might be tall or I might be short.
I might be strong or I may be weak.
I might walk or I might crawl
I may be rich or I may be poor
I may love and I may hate
I can be happy at times and sometimes nervous
Anxious, excited, sad, lonely, cheerful.

I could live in a big manor house
Or in a small cave with only a mouse.
I might live in a zoo full of animals of all sorts
Or in the middle of the jungle with a massive horse.
I may live in a hollowed-out tree, but I am still me.

I could be as lonely as a bird that's lost its friends
I could be one of a family that never ends
It could be just me and my parents
But we'd have loads of descendants.
It might be just me and my dad
It might just be me and my mum
Whoever I'm with, I'm always glad.

I might live in a country that's as big as can be!
I may live in a country that's smaller than me!
I might be lost in the unknown
I might be in Oz because of a cyclone
I may live anywhere, anywhere I please.
But I know I have not changed because I am
still me.

I know I have not changed and I never will.
I know I might look different
I might smell different
I might think differently.
But I am still me.

Eva Sloan (10)

This Is What I Love

I love how the sky is blue,
When clouds create phenomenal sights,
How the stars twinkle in the night sky,
And how the...

Animals are cool,
To pet some and stay away from others,
How lions roar and snore,
How dogs bark, to say hello.

How the internet is so fun
How you can type what you want,
How you can play different games,
Be anything you want.

How sports are great,
And how there are so many different sports,
And how you can skate on ice,
Float on water,
And tackle in rugby.

How you can find rhythm in music,
Where music inspires,

Where different genres allow you to escape to your own world.

How family pick you up,
How they push you to your limits,
How they always care.

How holidays come and go,
How they always have a meaning,
And relaxation for each one.

How dogs love to lick,
How they follow you everywhere,
How they love to fetch a ball,
How they never hold a grudge.

How I sleep at night free of sorrow,
How I dream of a new tomorrow,
As dreams come and go,
Reassured to wake to a better tomorrow.

How these little verses,
Have a message,
Embedded in their skin,
How life has no end,

How this poem is what I love,
So now, this is where we part.

Thomas Mathieson

This Is Me

Why do I find spellings so difficult, but others find them so simple?
Nanna tells me that I am brilliant at maths,
But sometimes I get a feeling that is not quite true.
Mummy declares that my writing is incredible,
But sometimes I worry she just says what I want to hear.
My brothers cackle that my jokes are hilarious,
But sometimes I know they are laughing at me.
Daddy gushes that I am confident at making friends,
But sometimes all I feel is shy.
My friends tell me I am fun and kind,
But sometimes I still find myself alone at playtime.
Why do I focus on the negatives,
When others see so many positives?
Perhaps it is time to accept that despite all the challenges I face,
I am unique and this is me.

Isabella Searle (9)

This Is Me

I am just a little girl, but I can make a difference,
By sharing my happiness rainbow,
Bringing cheer and joy to all,
Chasing away worry and woe.

So soak in red for reading,
Create your own magical place,
Be an emperor, adventurer or a wizard,
Or an astronaut blasting into space.

Splurge in orange, the joy of all things living,
Get a best pet friend of your own,
Fish, dogs, birds or frogs,
Make them your playmates and you will never be
alone.

Splash in the brilliance of sunshine yellow,
That pierces through the dark greys like an arrow,
Playing, gardening, swimming and picnicking,
Have fun to the fullest like there's no tomorrow.

Jump onto the greens,
Enjoy the Earth's nature,

Trees, plants, flowers and shrubs,
And all the living creatures.

Lose yourself in the indigo and blue skies,
Let the astronaut in you shine,
Wish upon a star, say hello to the man on
the moon,
Or just spot a constellation in your own time.

No rainbow is complete,
Without its violet,
That, for me, is my family,
Fantastic and my best asset.

This is me and my happiness rainbow,
Simple things that money can't buy,
Find your own,
And share the cheer and joy.

Nysa Valentine (9)

Oh, What A Brilliant Day!

Millions of presents at my door,
Now, I'm a millionaire,
Wrapped in the shimmering paper on the floor,
Ready for me to tear,
Oh, what a brilliant day!

Wow! The decorations make me feel like it's a real celebration,
Blue and purple balloons, and silver sparkling tinsel,
Everyone wearing party hats for this momentous occasion,
Me showing great appreciation is essential,
Oh, what a brilliant day!

Every colour of the rainbow is how I feel,
The luckiest girl in the world it seems,
As proud as a peacock on its heel,
From ear to ear, my grin beams,
Oh, what a brilliant day!

Heaps of wonderful cards,
Decorated with gleeful drawings,

From the darlings at my yard,
Created by the best earthlings,
Oh, what a brilliant day!

My birthday meal,
Burgers, chips and my favourite dip,
Oh, what a big deal,
The family made it feel all hip,
Oh, what a brilliant day!

My melodious birthday song,
Birthday cake on its way,
Everybody sings along,
How very loud are they,
Oh, what a brilliant day!

Yummy cake my mummy always bakes,
Bright candles sat on top,
Chocolatey and even scrumptious cupcakes,
Party poppers pop,
Oh, this is by far the most brilliant day!

Jemimah Rashid (11)

My Day

I just woke up buzzing from my dream,
Writhing and fumbling with a scream,
Calming down with a very funny meme.

My wonderful day has just begun,
Though going downstairs is not so fun.
With a crunch, my breakfast is now done.

After a shower, my uniform is ready,
Putting my socks on is not so steady,
Now I'm riding my bike to school already.

Now it's English and maths, not a bore,
Though I did have a quick snore.
After assembly, we get taught some more.

After break, we have to go in,
Time for history, learning about our kin.
Phew! It's lunch, time to eat amongst all the din.

Now some fun, we get to paint in art,
Ethan is drawing a gun and dart,
While Bruce and Jack paint rails and a cart.

Home time now, everyone flocks to their home,
While I show Mum my painting of a gnome,
At home, I put on my PJs and search on Chrome.

Time for my dinner, oh, it's heaven,
Lying in bed later, counting sheep up to seven,
Dreaming away, thinking I'm in Devon.

Vihaan George (10)

I Am Me

I am me,
A person,
A person with an ambition,
A person who has rights,
A person who does what they want and not just to
fit in,
Because I am me,

I am me,
A football-loving girl,
But will they ever accept a girl playing football?
I don't care if they don't,
I will just keep playing,
Because I am me,

I am me,
A loud person,
Too loud for my classmates,
I will just keep being loud,
As loud as thunder in a ruthless storm,
Because I am me,

I am me,
A commanding person,
Too commanding for my friends,
I will be commanding forever,
The leader of a pack on the football pitch,
Because I am me,

I am me,
A puffin girl,
Too crazy about puffins,
I will just keep loving these creatures,
As they are the animal for me,
Because I am me,

I am me,
A unique person,
A unique person who is what I want to be,
A unique person with a respect for friends,
A unique person with a love for the world,
Because I am me.

Isla Scott (12)

The Forgotten Planet That Became A Star

Body relaxed, mind calm
The school day behind me
Back in Mum's arms
I fall in my bed, head resting on my pillow
I know it off by heart
A gift from Mum and Dad around the time of their wedding
"I love you to the moon and back," and I know they do
The room glows around me, the stickers on my wall
The sun, Venus, our Earth, Mercury, Jupiter, Uranus, Saturn, Mars, Neptune
And finally, the moon, like the one, they love me too
I think about Pluto, the forgotten planet, and I remember Mum's reminder that it is not forgotten, it's a star
Just like me, renamed to become something more special
Like the stars that shine on my ceiling, the ones that drift me off to sleep

They're beautiful, still burning bright
And so many are all together that they'll never
have to feel alone
I dream of how my mum found me and of the
memories we've already made
My favourite one at the beach, mum wrapping me
up in a towel warmed by the sun
It reminds me of how I feel now in my duvet, only a
lot more grown
Pluto was a planet that became a star, not
forgotten
Just like me.
This is me.

Thomas Butler (10)

All About Lucas Liu

L oving towards my family, because they always protect and care about my well-being.

U nderstand there are many poorly people, so I aspire to be a doctor, because to cure the sick is as meaningful as donating clothes to Africa.

C autious and careful like an affectionate cat with my surroundings, by watching out for danger on roads and not talking to strangers.

A ppreciating that I have good health and thanking God for everything I am blessed with in my life.

S uper creative and daring at Minecraft, it is my favourite computer game, which is full of mining, building, and exploring.

L earning is improving my knowledge, I love attending school every day, especially in my Design Technology lesson, where I get to make different colourful models.

I mmense interests in piano and trumpet because I love the magical sounds which are like fairy-tale music, enjoy chess challenges and learning Mandarin as a second language.

U nafraid of new challenges and love to explore
   new sports, such as rugby, skiing and kayaking.

Lucas Liu (8)

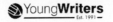

This Is M.E.

Today I feel tired,
Yesterday I felt tired,
The day before I felt tired.
It's annoying,
I'm fed up with it,
I want it to stop.
I try to fight it,
But it gets the better of me.

It's an unseen enemy,
A silent foe,
An evil whisper draining me.
I put my mind in a book,
I forget about the attack,
But when I stop,
I go into the battle once again.

Writing is hard,
Thinking of describing words is hard,
This tiredness makes everything hard.
My head is hurting,
The pain swirling round.

My feet have a mind of their own
Often hurting me and making me groan.
But it doesn't help.

I want to burn with energy,
Soon I hope to win,
To be victorious against this tiredness.
To turn the tables on this traitor,
With a glint in my eye,
To run and climb trees with ease.
I do not know what will come,
But I really hope my wish will come true.

Bram Thompson (9)

Truly Me

I am unique and good at different things,
I love art and the joy that it brings.
It makes you feel free, no perfect design
But instead of it being chosen, you get to decide.
I also like sports, it makes me feel fit,
it makes my heart beat very quick.
You don't have to be great, but you just need to try,
And once you have learnt, you will fly.
Another thing I enjoy to do is read,
People don't see it, it's not what they see.
I get lost in the words and the pattern it makes,
And when it intensifies, my head quakes.
I am obsessed with writing poems, especially ones that rhyme,
I like how the words flow and how they keep in time.
I like to read poems and write them too;
My favourite ones are the ones that are true.
I could keep going on about what I like,
But if I did, I'd be here all night.

Now I've had a feel of poetry, I must finish off and go to sleep.
This is what I like and see, this is what is truly me.

Lydia Gebrihiwot (9)

The Day That Kindness Came To Visit

Kindness floated down my street,
With clouds beneath her feet.
As a dove's feather floated down on the floor,
She skipped across my driveway and knocked on my door.

Her eyes were yellow like the sun,
And her hair was tucked back into a neat bun.
She had on a lovely pink dress,
And had told me it was her very best.

When I saw her, I felt happy,
But I had to remember I was changing my sister's nappy!
I rushed downstairs to open the door,
As soon as I set my sister on the floor.

When she came in, she took out some flour,
So quick I swore she had a superpower.
Then we made a cake for tea,
In the shape of a buzzing bee.

In the late afternoon,
I took out a spoon,
To make Kindness some rainbow tea.
Then we had some cake and said goodbye,
Next time we'd meet in Normandy.

She remains me of my older sister Georgie,
Hey, wait a minute, where is she?

Kweli Baillie (10)

Who Am I?

Life was happy,
Life was good,
That's what I thought where I was stood,
Having a family and a friend,
Is this where my journey would end?
It started with infected fleas
People got sick and fell to their knees

Headaches, fevers and chills
Suffering because we couldn't afford the bills
Red crosses painted on your doors
Am I next? Nobody knows
A life in quarantine
Not a single soul to be seen
Dark blotches on your skin
Eating rations from a rusty old tin

Living scared and in fear
"These are our lives," you can hear
Getting angry, wanting to blame
Life will never be the same
Hold your loved ones

Hold them close
Our old life we missed the most
The world fell still
No antidote nor a pill

The Plague had gone away
It is remembered 'til this very day
With no possibility to become immune
Who am I? I'm Thomas J Noon.

Thomas J Noon

Me!

I hear everything,
Every thought, every emotion,
In the silence of my room.
Writing down the words,
Feeling every line,
As I listen to nothing

I smell everything,
Every flower, every person who walks by,
As I prance in my shoes,
And tap my toes,
Listening to the melody of each happy note

I taste everything,
Every memory, every slice of cake,
Savouring every bite,
As I catch the breeze between my teeth,
Climbing trees as high as a skyscraper,
Travelling along paths without a map,
Wondering what lay ahead

I feel everything,
Every angry pout, every laughing moment,

In the chaos of my mind,
As I try to soothe the manic,
With a song,
With a colour,
With a rest,
With a drink,
Emptying my mind of its constant buzzing

I touch everything,
Every texture, every new beginning
As I roll the dice around my palm.

Madeline Roberts (11)

This Is Me

This is me
My life is a busy painting
I paint it all these different shades
I paint it a warming red
As red as a Canadian maple leaf I use to make
maple syrup
I paint it a rustic orange
As orange as an autumn sunset I watch at the cold
beach
I paint it a joyful yellow
As yellow as a beautiful dandelion under the lovely
sun
I paint it a buzzing green
As green as sweet blades of spring grass with bees
flying around
I paint it a summer-sky blue
As blue as a tropical sea where I might swim or sail
happily
I paint it a calming violet
As violet as the brightest amethyst I have on my
necklace
I paint it a loving pink

As pink as blushing cheeks, I get when I like what
people say to me
I paint my picture all the shades of life as I find out
things about myself
It may be weird to other people
But I see it like this and think it's true
Because this is me.

Daisy Clarke (8)

This Is Me!

A question floats in my mind
I fall into a deep abyss
The query is who am I?
Who is me?

I think about my enjoyable hobbies
Singing
Dancing
Painting
And more

This is unsatisfying me
I think deeper
Even more than before
Like my love and affection for words
But the words drift in all directions, moving away

Am I alone?
I have my mum
My dad
My friends and family
But without these people and things, who am I?

A girl, left to think
Of this wide world
Single, solo

No, I am way more than that
I am a girl
Who is bold and fearless as a lion
Bright and glowing as a star
Smart yet curious about this universe

Who am I?
Who is me?
Well I got the answer
I am...
Powerful
Friendly
Beautiful (in and out)
Kind
Smart
Adventurous
That is who I am
That is me!

Malavika Nair (10)

Fervour

I will remain by your side and as your
acquaintance,
My dominance as a mathematician is invincible,
I warn you of the consequences of competing with
me,
My energy and eagerness none can handle.

Knowledgeable, talented, and joyful together,
Cherishing time with rivals and producing more
pleasure,
I ask for someone unique who flickers like a star,
Bold, reckless and follows their desire,

Switching like the firmament from day to night,
Someone to pinion the despicable neighbourhood,
To enlighten a realm superior to the universe,
With suppleness and concentration, if only we
understood.

Finest moments presented through me,
Something I acknowledge, never done before,
Moral principles led me to this day,
I present my honourable ownership of these
capabilities,

If no one stood up, it belongs to me
Huffing with tremulous hands and teary eyes,
The last thing I will always commemorate,
Not only am I passionate, but *I am a writer too!*

Dua E Zainab (11)

This Is Me

This is me, this is me,
All about my life and my glee.
I will tell you about my ups and downs,
All about my smiles and all my frowns.
Now sit back and enjoy my story,
As I tell you how I rose to glory.

When I was young, I thought I was the odd
one out,
That not many liked me, and I had my doubts.
I tried my hardest to be the best,
But I knew I had failed my quest.
I just wanted people to see,
That I am Tate, and this is me.

When I was older, I had had enough,
So, I tried even harder and showed off my stuff,
I put my name down for a job I hoped to get.
Do you think I got it? You bet!
I was head boy, happy and free,
And I could show everyone that I am Tate, and this
is me.

That was me, yes, that was me,
Oh, how my life was filled with glee.
About my ups and my downs,
And all my smiles and my frowns.
So, think of this poem when you go to sleep tonight,
That even when things look dark, it will all be alright.

Tate Hassall (11)

What Is In My Life?

What is in my life?
Heartache, morose, grim
Dark, lifeless, dim
Stress, pressure, struggle.
These were the things that defined me,
These were the things that confined me.
Everything in this life I had to juggle
The work, school, tuitions
There was so much to do.
To remember nouns, verbs, definitions.
There was always tension in the air
There was worry, without compare;
Hatred flooded through my veins
Like a river that was going to overflow.
These emotions would forevermore remain,
And that river would forever grow.

But my heart is a diamond in the rough.
My mind is sharp,
My will is tough.
Though the peaks and valleys will come and go
These emotions that I'll always know.

Love, attention, happiness and thrill
Laughter, enthusiasm, creativity and skill.
The bright path ahead will always be clear
All you have to do is stay and be near.

Aadya Arya (11)

The Tale Of Me

My tale unfolds
Slinkily slithering
White and grey
I start to shrink
Day by day, bit by bit, smaller and smaller and
growing fur
Fur grey like gloomy clouds
My whiskers appear
Thin and long like needles
Day by day,
Bit by bit,
Longer and longer
With my whiskers I sense much better than I did
before
My ears extend they change into something fluffy,
just like my fur.
Every drop of water,
Every touch, I can hear all that in just a twitch.
I look at my paws, white and grey
I look at my claws, sharp and shiny
I look at my tail, graceful and pretty
I balanced using a tail,

I walked using paws,
I sensed using whiskers,
I listened through pointed ears,
My life became a story, told in many ways,
But this one is a poem...

Rosanna Ren (9)

This Is Me!

This is me!
My passion.
My life.
My story.
Come join me on this journey.
My passion is big,
Bold and great,
Like a gorilla fighting an ape!
My passion is active and on the go.
Although I am a girl,
I am no boy's shadow!
I grow like a flower.
I have plenty of power!
Yes,
I need practise, but I hope and I know I will grow
like a cactus!
I am an actress in the making, but I am changing
and rearranging,
People's minds, to make them realise girls, boys,
Women, men,
Female, male,

Ladies *and* gentlemen are equal whoever they may be!

My passion is football,
But wait, there's more.
The worries itch like a twitch on the pitch!

Girls need to rise up and feel confident.
You *can* be dominant!
So, come on girls.
We can do this!
I can be whatever I want to be!
And so can you!

Maya Oxborrow (9)

This Is Me

I like to dance,
I like to prance.
I like chocolate, chips and cheese.
I like sucking lemons or limes,
And I definitely don't like peas!
I like cats!
Especially tabbies,
And I definitely don't like rats!
I am very funny,
I am described as sunny!
I am nature's child,
I like to explore the wild.
My favourite colour is indigo,
I like to watch a show called Lingo!
Lingo is hosted by Adil Ray,
My favourite subject in school is clay.
I like to pretend I am a witch or wizard,
I also like to eat delicious lemon curd.
I am afraid of spiders and the dark,
I like to visit our local park.

I also like to read and write stories and poems too, I hope you have enjoyed this poem I have written for you!

Zaynah Jabeen-Iqbal (7)

Seven Years At Alexandra

Seven years at Alexandra,
And now the year is coming to a close,
The time has come to say goodbye,
To my friends, teachers and outgrown school
clothes.

Although it might be worrying,
Excitement floods through,
New friends, new lessons,
What's not to love about a school that's
brand new?

I'm looking forward to making new friends,
on the first day of school,
Not sure what's in store,
A brand-new classroom,
And a whole lot more.

I have so many questions,
How this year will be,
A brand-new adventure,
I'll have to wait and see.

Yay,
I'll be no more,
A primary-schooler,
Looking forward to at last being a high-schooler.

Seven years at Alexandra,
Now the year is at its close,
The time is here to say goodbye,
To my friends, teachers and outgrown school
clothes.

Ayza Hanif (10)

Rising Up

You may mock, hit, push me down,
With desperate cries, my spirit dies down.
You may gossip about me with horrid lies,
But like the waves thundering forward, I rise.

Just like time ticking away,
With the strength of a whale on a bay.
Just like dreams flying at moonrise,
I rise.

Did you want to see me crumble?
Maybe a little tumble?
What about your lies?
Can you see my demise?

On the cracked surface, still clashing, I rise.
Ascending up - crumbling, smashing like armies
fighting, I rise.
I am a stallion, thundering the ground,
I am a mustang, crashing around.

Abandoning times of spiteful grief and fear, I rise.
In a world as delicate as a tear, I rise.

From my thoughts I dream for, I have to bear how it seems,
I am the hope, the gleam, the power of my dreams.
I rise.
I rise.
I rise.

Idris Jones (9)

Happiness

Happiness lives in me,
At the top of my heart,
In me anger will never start,
Anger always lets me be,

Happiness is when people let me play,
On a bright sunny day,
This is stuff that makes me cheery,
When I am happy, I eat a cherry,

Happiness plays a major part in my life,
It makes me feel so alive,
It sometimes makes me be excited,
When my friend asked me out and I was smitten,
that's what it's like,

Happiness is not bought in a supermarket,
It's when you buy your favourite food in the
market,
When you go home, you have big smile on your
face,
The very next day, you complete your bookcase,

Happiness makes me laugh so hard,
I become red and charred,
That night I had a sound sleep with a sweet dream,
The very next day, it's my birthday, the cake I got
had whipped cream.

Aaditri Manjunath (8)

Is This Me?

Is this me, bold and bright?
Is this me, a sheer delight?
Is this me, who thinks she's smart?
Is this me, with a kind heart?
Is this me, who likes to twirl and prance?
Is this me, who likes to dance?

Could it be me, who gets scared sometimes?
Could it be me, who tries not to cry?
Could it be me, who tries to be strong, even when I
get things wrong?

I'm sure it's me who is a good friend,
I'm sure it's me who would 'take the knee' and
bend,
I'm sure with me that change will happen,
I'm sure with my poetry, I will get to Manhattan.
I know it's me who is confident and funny,
One day, I hope to make lots of money,
Eco-warrior, champion of peace; that's me,
I pick up rubbish in our community.

It's me!

This *is* me!

Alara Logie (8)

This Is Me!

Ishaq Munir is the name,
Playing football is my game.

To Bowker Vale School I go,
Time for register, sit in a row.

Ready, respectful and safe are the rules,
Those who don't follow are the fools.

Super strong and fast mind,
That's me, smart and kind.

Off to the police force one day soon,
Missions needed to be completed by noon.

Need to be the best version of myself,
Aim for the highest book on the shelf.

Lamborghini is the dream,
Eating lots of waffles and cream.

My birthday is in June,
I'll keep partying till I see the moon.

Family and friends are important to me,
Living together in a house by the sea.
This is me.

Ishaq Munir

My Magic Box

Inspired by 'The Magic Box' by Kit Wright

I will put in the box,
My thin lips as pink as a strawberry milkshake,
My freckles like sprinkles and glitter on a cupcake,
as cute as a puppy.
And my black hair as shiny as a diamond and as
black as night.

I will put in the box,
My soft voice as quiet as a giraffe or birds in the
forest and hibernating animals,
My sweet, kind and caring acts, looking after my
friends and sisters,
And my love of art and drawing happy things.

I will put in the box,
Dreams of trips to Spain on the swirly, whirly slide
and the swimming pool at a hotel,
A snuggly bed with all my toys, slowly drifting to
sleep,
And baking chocolate chip cookies, fluffy cakes
and puffy cupcakes for friends and family.

My box is my body.
This is me.

Libby Lethbridge (9)

This Is Me

I am awesome in every single way,
I am determined, I am bright and I never go astray.
Kindness is what I am - my best quality,
Next up in line comes wonderful equality.

In everything I do, I am vigilant,
I am not at all belligerent,
I always do my best in life,
I'll do anything to stop strife.

My family and friends are what matter to me,
They are always there to support me, you see,
Always there to hold my back,
There is nothing that these people lack.

I like football, I like cricket,
Always aiming to take the wicket,
I am sporty, I am fast,
Oh - it's PE at last!

I am special, I am awesome,
I am one in a million,

In all this world, there's only one of me,
And that's what makes me special.

Archit Shenoy (11)

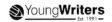

Things You Need To Know About Orla

My jelly body wiggles,
Like the seaweed in the sea,
The pillow cheeks upon my face,
Are as squidgy as can be.

My mermaid hair is long and wavy
But sometimes is a mess,
However much my mother asks,
I will not wear a dress.

Music flows inside my veins,
I love to sing and dance,
Holidays are amazing too,
Next time, I'm off to France!

I can sometimes be annoying,
Asking questions day and night,
But I know my family love me,
And will always hold me tight.

Crunching crisps and watching films,
Makes me happy every day,
Cuddling my kittens,
Makes my troubles go away.

Now you've reached the poem's end,
I hope you've got to know me.
One day, maybe, we will be friends,
But let's just wait and see!

Orla Salmon (8)

In The Dark There Is Light

There once was a girl,
Named Joe Malone,
She was sadly all alone,

One fateful day,
Darkness came out to play,
Infecting all to be seen,
Quarantine seemed to be mean,
That made Joe sad but not mad,
Soon after, she got a bunny,
That was oh so funny,
She spent time with her family,
And lived happily,

You may think, *why would she be happy*,
Living in a time of tragedy,
As she had nowhere to go?
But the love in her family started to grow,
As she made cakes with her mother,
And played games with her brother,
That's the life Joe wanted to lead,

As the virus fades, we all yell, "Hooray!"
Soon the virus will go away,
And remember, in darkness there will always
be light,
Goodnight.

Fausta Kiselyte (11)

Unity Is Strength

One fine day, I found myself surrounded with short,
horny elf-like creatures
Plagued by a vile villain, they pleaded for help in
their strident times
Being benevolent, I pledged to unshackle them
from the curse of the monstrous mammoth
In the blink of an eye, emerged before me a world
filled with flying cars, houses and time machines
Amalgam of brain and unison is the only possible
rescue
Moral of 'unity is strength' helped to stand upfront
in queue
Sun, moon, star energy and death rays with the
whole determined team, attacked the deadly devil
'United we stand, divided we fall' brought the end
of the wretched evil!
Triumphantly the team accorded me their king
But alas, I woke up in the morning!

Parth Aggarwal (10)

A Peek Into My World!

I am Aakriti,
Good at heart,
I'm very smart and not the best at art,
Industrious and compassionate are just a few
words.
Adventurous and bold are what I am when I am
not the class nerd!
I hate when spine-chilling spiders crawl around,
When people I know put me down.
But what really puts a smile on my face,
Is when I get to eat a scrumptious chocolate cake!

When I grow up, I aspire to be a great author,
I am an only child, an exquisite daughter!
A beloved best friend, a remarkable pupil,
I pass time doing quirky doodles!
There is nothing I would change about my unique
personality,
I am Aakriti and this is me.

Aakriti Barpanda (10)

Be True, Be You, Be Proud

People hide behind their masks, like a tortoise
hides in his shell,
Not wishing for the world to see what truly lies
beneath,
The truth, the fear, the vulnerability.

We paint a picture of a perfect life,
Photographs, messages, social media: all
portraying perfection.
When you look at these, it makes you feel jealous,
when in reality it's an album of lies.

You may like to pose,
You may like to boast,
You may like to hide the truth,
But you are you.

Remember to be true to yourself,
The imperfections are perfect,
They shape who we are,
We learn through the events that happen,
The ups, the downs.
Our real colours show in the end.

We are all a perfect version of ourselves.
Be true,
Be you,
Be proud.

Katie Thornton (9)

This Is Me

This poem is all about me
Starting off with my family
I live with my mum, dad and sister too
I have a super neighbour whose name is Sue!
And had a cat called Baloo

I love to dance with my dance club at school
I think my moves are super cool
Art is my passion
Such as designing fashion
My dream is to fly
I'm honest and don't lie

I'm confident and rarely sad
I think my maths is pretty bad
English is my best subject
Wanna know something you wouldn't suspect?
I love fairground rides big and small
And swinging ones, short and tall
I love all nature, animals and plants
I was one when I started to dance

I make mistakes occasionally
But that's okay, because
This is me

Jacey May Gardiner (10)

Anger

I have a monster bubbling up inside.
And when he's in a hurry, he'll always want a ride.
He is spiky and scary with the most enormous
fangs
But they do not compare to the pain of his pangs.
Anger doesn't like it when people call him names
And as punishment for that, he'll chase you down
the lanes!
He is the most ferocious emotion that there is
And if you dare touch his things, he'll scream that
they're his!
People don't like me when I'm angry, cos my
monster shouts at them
And sometimes they ignore me even if I go, "Eh-
hem."
My monster is very lonely and wishes for a friend
But his search is thankfully complete as this poem
comes to an end.

Olivia O'Neill (9)

Does Race Matter?

So what If I'm black or mixed-race?
Respecting people is the real race,
My religion, my goals,
I'm a black pigeon flying through holes.
What's black is black, what's white is white.
Equality is what is right.
My roots are England
My roots are Africa,
Windrush washed up on the shore.
Us black and mixed-race people must be shown more.
Do some of us really have to be poor?
Our personalities are us, is that fair?
This world is something we must share.
There are black heroes we look up to,
If you want to, you can too.
There is one hero called Wangari Maathai,
And there is also Benjamin Zephaniah,
So does race matter to all of us?
Yes, it does; Now, Follow us.

Harris Katiisa Cheney (9)

The Morning

Waking up at 6am to my friend saying, "Get up, get up."
I refuse to get up, then he slams the door, then he comes running back.
"Now what?" he gives me a look.
I say, "Again?"
"Yes," he says, with a familiar look.
I get up with a shake,
Grabbing a coat with a small hood,
Setting off with a rock of luck. Running around with a smile,
When an idea pops up, I shout, "I know where she is!"
My friend comes running back, I found her at the caravan.
Oh. We head back with a look, I hope we get cake,
He says, "You can read minds."
I say, "Maybe," with a laugh.

Myah Jones (9)

I Am The Sea

I am the sea, vast and grey
"Do I sleep?" you say, nay
"Do I weep?" you say, only when you see the salty spray
"Am I deep?" you say, very deep under the surface I lay

I am the sea, spread under the moon
"Will I tire?" you say, soon
"Will I dry?" you say, in a thousand years at noon
"Do I float?" you say, like a balloon

I am the sea, beautiful and blue
"Am I old?" you ask, well I am not new
"Do I wreck ships?" you ask, I swallow the crew
"Do I bask in the sun?" you ask, I do, I do

I am the sea
Fish in my belly
Boats on my back
I'm waiting for a coast-sized snack!

Mary Willan (11)

This Is Me

I dream that I live in a castle,
With my teachers, Mrs Timms and Mrs Marshall,
I dream that I fly among clouds,
And melodies are blasting loud.

My mum, my dad, my sis,
Fill me with lots of bliss,
Life at home, as the youngest,
I try not to be a pest.

I love playing the piano,
That's something for you to know,
The endless world of music,
Too good, I'll never get sick.

I think school is super fun
And with my friends, I play and run,
Some people think they're too cool for school,
But in the end, kids rule!

My favourite hobby is crafts,
Always glueing lots of pieces and parts,

I'll make something for you, eagerly,
And hand it to you quickly.

Aadharshya Maran (9)

The Magic Of Games

Enveloped in another world
I am as happy as can be
I don't need to catch a plane to be a million
miles away

Zooming across the bright blue sky
To collect the last golden puzzle piece
Avoiding cows meandering across the track
To win the race and raise the cup
Shooting down skeleton foe
To smash my high score to smithereens
Melting ice blocks with laser beams
To search for the hidden treasure chest
Speeding down the steep slope
To expertly land a big jump

Getting frustrated when I fall off the ledge
Jumping for joy as I reach a new level
I love my games console.

Poppy Picton (9)

My Culture: Indian

Indian is being diverse, dedicated, determined
Indian is having affection and love
Indian is growing up with contentment and stories
Indian is being blessed with happiness

Being Indian is needing equal opportunities
Being Indian is like a shattered mirror
One side of sophistication, hiding the pain
Being Indian is closing your eyes and ears
Ignoring hatred and discrimination
It is the sound of criticism ringing like bells

Indian is being me
Surrounded by family and friends
Accepting those with different races, genders
and wealth
Indian is in our blood, our soul and our mind
It is having beauty with a drop of pain
Culture is me and culture is you.

Aaina Chopra (11)

I Am Me!

Like the rose in a field of pansies,
I stand out from the rest.
With my life and the people I've come across,
I found out I am blessed.

As bright as a light bulb, some may say,
Or as loyal as they come.
I'll heal your sadness with a smile
To make you feel less glum.

When people say they're not worth it,
And they feel down or blue,
I tell them that if I'm special,
Then they are special too.

My friends would call me funny.
My parents say I'm unique.
In my teacher's words, I'm creative,
But in my words, I am me!

Naomi Matthews (11)

Horses

Every day, when the horses are up,
They're saddled and are ready for a day of work.
Some horses are ridden,
While others pull carts.
Some enjoy it, while some do not.

All horses have personalities;
Moody, silly, whacky, lazy,
And all horses walk differently;
Fast, slow, steady, bouncy.

While some horses like to run,
Others like to take it slow.

They're all different sizes too;
Tiny, small, big, giant.
They eat all kinds of food;
Sugar, hay, apples, carrots.

And even though they're all different,
I love them all!

Zoha Mehdi (9)

A Riddle

As fast as lightning he zooms past
Beating the defenders, not failing to surpass
Left and right, he dances with the ball.
"Come on, shoot!" they all call.
"Give us a goal!"
When the referee shouts with all his might
He stands up to take the penalty with delight
Concentrating cautiously, he lifts his boot
And shoots!
"Copland hero!" they chant merrily.
"Our saviour!"
Jamaican race he shares
Which is something about which he cares
Wearing number ten
He stands as strong as Big Ben

Who is he?

Abiwaran Parameswaran (11)

Me, Me, That's Who I'm Going To Be

Every time I stand out loud,
I'm going to be proud.
My unique way will be a booming sound.
When you hear, it will be profound.
Me, me, that's who I'm going to be!

With my mum, I like to bake,
And my favourite dessert is a flapjack or cake.
I love swimming, but not in a lake.
So many crafts are what I make.
I love being me, for goodness' sake!
Me, me, that's who I'm going to be!

My favourite vegetables are peas.
When I smile, I like to say, "Cheese."
I'm afraid of wasps and all bees.
In forest school, I love to climb trees.
Me, me, that's who I'm going to be!

Griffith-Nmaju (9)

This Is Me

If I were a thing
I would choose to be
All my favourite things
That make me, me!

If I were a flower,
I would be a rose,
So resilient,
Just like me!

If I were a fruit,
I would be a strawberry,
So very sweet,
Just like me!

If I were an animal,
I would be a puppy,
So very cheeky,
Just like me!

If I were a colour,
I would be bright pink,

So very confident,
Just like me!

If I were a pudding,
I would be a cake,
So very marvellous,
Just like me!

If I were a shoe,
I would be an old trainer,
So very trustworthy,
Just like me!

If I were a child,
I would be Darcey,
So very kind,
Because it's me!

Darcey Hassett (8)

Virat

Intelligent, honest, kind, thoughtful

Who loves family, school and pizza
Who enjoys swimming, reading and writing
Who fears the dark, deep waters and the bad
Who believes in everything he does
Who wonders if he can count the number of cars in the world
Who plans to be a scientist, create magical and mysterious fluids
Who feels excited about holidays, competition and new learning
Who always helps and tries his best
Also

V ictorious
I ncredible inventor
R apid
A dventurous
T remendous.

Virat Manchambatla (7)

My Brother

M akes me laugh all the time
Y uck, he hates chocolate

B est at hide-and-seek... not
R ides his police bike at the park
O n holiday, he loves the caravan
T alks and talks and talks and talks
H e waves to the firefighters as they pass
E ats lots of bananas
R uns very fast

B rothers are awesome, except for the mess
E xcellent at playing cars
N oisy when I'm trying to read
J am sandwiches are his favourite lunch
I s very, very cheeky.

Emily Norton (8)

Isabelle Chaplin

I love Lego, English and Harry Potter!
S illiness is key!
A rtistic in drawing!
B eing kind makes people happy!
E ncanto is brilliant!
L aughter is great!
L ove a Disney movie!
E njoys 'We Don't Talk About Bruno'!

C uddles with teddies are so fun!
H appy when friends are around!
A nd flowers are cute!
P lushies, plushies and more plushies!
L ike books, kinda; I would rather Encanto!
I ce cream,
N uts about this list!

Chaplin (9)

Underneath

Under my shirt is my skin
And under my skin is my heart.

Under my heart is a roast dinner
And under that is typing a story on my laptop.
Under that is Zoe - who moved away
And under that is playing Surviving on Norwich.
Under that is making my bed
And under that is my dream about Granny driving
a digger.

Under that is playing on Florida's beaches
And under that is dressing up as Fireman Sam.
Under that is my dream to be an author
And under that is my lesson to be honest.

Under that is when I kicked a girl from my school in
the playground
And under that is summer.
These are my memories.

Audrey Laurent (10)

I Am Issy

I am pretty like a bird,
flying in the sky.
My fluffy, curly hair makes me feel special.
It's not frizzy, it's not straight,
it's in-between, it's great!

I am brave
but I fear climbing a tall mountain...
I worry my mum may catch COVID again.
However, I am strong,
I am Issy!

I dream to be an astronaut.
I wonder if I can get better at gymnastics.
I can do vault,
I can do floor,
I can spin and twirl,
I love to tumble,
it feels like rolling down a hill.

I am loving,
I am caring,

I am creative.
I am Issy!

Isabel Greenwood (8)

Elinor - This Is Me

I want to be a doctor, making people strong.
I want to help people, all day long.

I am still young, and I've got a lot of the way to go,
But I will work hard and never say no.

As bright as the sun, as dark as the night,
I try to be a star, making the light.

I love unicorns and fairies too,
Even though I'm eight, I still think they're true.

I game on the Xbox and always try to win,
And travel on Roblox with cool hair and a big grin.

I go to bed a little bit late,
But I still wake up feeling great.

I start every day optimistically,
Put this all together and this poem is me.

Elinor Keller (8)

Happiness

Happiness lives in the brightest of skies,
Where everybody laughs and smiles,
As she skips down the sunny streets,
You can see her happiness for miles.

The luscious colours,
The prettiest pink, opulent orange and sunniest
yellow,
It feels like eating birthday cake,
Or sweets, or chocolate or marshmallow.

She's the sun through your windows,
She's the smile on your face,
She's the warm feeling inside of you,
When your plan falls into place.

If she's missing for a while,
You know she will soon be back,
Unless you fill your mind with happiness,
Then sadness will not attack.

Arun Darar (10)

Recipe For Ola!

A library of infinite books,
And a pair of glasses to complete the look!
Make space for the piano and violin,
With music, you're sure to have a grin.
Now it's time for cycling and swimming,
No regular exercise? Are you kidding?
Create time for writing and drawing,
Great skills and more so very calming.
Spend time with friends and family.
That's my way of ensuring I live happily.
Garnish it all with laughter and smiles,
And a sense of love that goes on for miles.
Stir them all together and that makes... *me!*

Ola Ukoha (10)

Wonderful Me

This is me; I am truly kind.
I am terribly busy; I have a lot on my mind.
Every day I have a bath or a shower,
Looking after myself, it's just girl power.
If you have ever met me,
You'll know my lucky number is three!
I have brown hair and blue eyes
I'd never let you swat a fly...
That is because I love animals of all different sizes,
Each one is a unique handful of surprises.
These things are what make me happy
Running and writing; after all, this is me!
So close your eyes and count to three,
You have finished this poem all about me.

Nia Vale (9)

Me

Writing poems is my favourite thing to do
As well as reading a good book
And coming up with my own stories too
And meeting my cousin at the cafe, the Nook

There are some styles of poetry I haven't tried yet
One of those is a villanelle
But if I tried hard, I bet
I could write one of those as well

I have a cat, she is called Tarka
From an otter she got her name
Some of her fur is dark, the rest is darker
For broken objects, she is usually to blame

My favourite game is Man Bites Dog
We play it really quite a lot
I ride my bike, but not in the fog
A little brother I have got.

Eva Langridge (9)

Fear

Fear lurks in unlikely places, like the
Basement and under your bed.
Fear roams amongst things
Which make your body feel like lead.

Fear triggers ceased up muscles,
Unleashes panic, causes sweat.
Fear makes your insides feel like they've been
Trapped inside a net.

Sometimes you know fear's coming, but
There are other times you don't.
Sometimes fear goes away quickly, sometimes it
Simply won't.

The cure to fear is simple, though:
Soothing words, cuddles, a mug of cocoa.
But I just want to make it clear:
I am not a prisoner of fear!

Anna Donovan (10)

All About Me

A mazing and incredible, is that the person you need?

L ook no further... That's me!

L isten up! Imagine someone who has an amazing dream.

A dream that's so mysterious, you have no idea.

B ut there will be a time when that dream has to go up in a puff of smoke

O r it will go on your bookshelves. You've got it; I love books!

U nlimited hope is what I need.

T o be in my own dream.

M aybe I'll face hardship,

E ventually I'll reach my goals!

Musa Muhammad (8)

Willow Pillow And Karate-Skilled Kaspar

My cat's name is Willow,
She's as soft as a pillow
She's obviously tough,
As she can survive the rough
An operation cone around her head
Strained position even when she's in bed.
Her fur is a chocolate black,
Willow is a rather beautiful cat.
Her eyes are an amber yellow
And her brother is here to say hello.
His name is Kaspar,
He's a cheeky little rascal.
With his speckled tabby coat
He loves having a stroke.
He attacks all the pens
And digs into cushions to make snug dens!

Esmay Steward (11)

This Is Me!

I am loving, caring and kind,
Someone like me is so hard to find.

My favourite subject is art,
Because I draw from the heart.

My favourite hobby is to bake,
Because I like delicious cakes.

Being a teacher is the dream,
Spending my day working as a team.

I like to go out to eat,
Because friends and family I get to meet.

Going to the beach is great fun,
You get to enjoy the sea, sands and sun!

My favourite animal is a monkey,
Because they are very funky.

These are all my favourite things,
I love the joys my life brings.

Spreading my wings, flying free.
This is me!

Fatima Mahmood (8)

My Granny

I have an awesome granny,
She's very small and brown,
And when I come to see her,
I never see her frown.

When I go to her house,
She cooks me scrumptious food,
And when the smell hits your nose,
You can't have an attitude.

She came from Trinidad,
A place far, far away,
She came to study nursing,
And she also came to stay.

I adore my granny's culture,
It's super, spicy cool,
You eat mangoes and curry,
You go to a beach, not a pool.

So those of you with a granny,
Write a poem about them,

Maybe yours is English,
But mine is a Caribbean gem!

Scarlett Little-Kerr

This Is Me

This is me, all I need is here,
With friends and family that's a cheer!
Come join me take a seat,
For this amazing feast,
I'm not perfect or an amazing person,
My life won't worsen,
I am unique and special,
However I have a lot of potential.

I like spicy stuff, many people do,
Guess what my favourite colour is, it's ocean blue!
I don't like fish or gravy,
I really like daisies,
I love maths,
It makes me go crazy!
Don't judge me or anyone,
Just let them have fun.

Warizah Fatma

Cats Deserve To Sit On Mats

When I finish my book's last chapters
I love to look at Unicode characters
I dislike entering some competitions
Because they raise my suspicions
I adore cats and bats
But not gnats!
If I ever had a cat
I would always let it sit on a mat.
If I were an important queen,
I would order everyone not to eat a runner bean!
I am fond of Japan's cherry trees,
But sadly, I am not fond of Japan's peas.
So now you know a little about me,
Why don't you drink some of my famous mint tea?

Selma Abdullah (9)

What My Violin Means To Me

I pick up my violin and there's no end,
Jiving and dancing,
Sad and happy, romance and rock,
You never know what my violin is going to play today.

When I play, my violin sounds as calm as the ocean waves,
Lapping on a sandy beach,
As graceful as a swift in flight,
And as sweet as a nightingale.

As you see, my violin means a lot to me,
It fills my heart with love and joy.

My violin is worth diamonds and gold to me.
It is made with love, joy, peace, and kindness.
The music it makes is worth listening to.
It is beautiful and I love it!

Neev Kaur-Chakravarti (8)

This Is Me!

This is me,
I am sometimes as angry as a boiling kettle and as happy as a blossoming flower.
I am a bit messy and that's a bit silly.
Everyone is unique, just like me!
I am a bit silly and it's naughty to me and more!
I am as adventurous as Harry Potter.
I am excited for many, many things, there is no ending to how many excitements I have.
I am as awesome as an awesome sticker.
I am fun, I am just like fun games like Minecraft.
I am as friendly and courteous as our 'Mother Earth'.
This is me!

Akshath Bandreddi (9)

Glistening Like A Huge Gold Coin

The sun was shining,
The trees were twirling.
In the gentle breeze,
All was at ease.
Extinguishing all the darkness
By burning every disease.
The gargantuan ball of fire,
A servant of God's desire.
This is what I want to be...
The one who radiates and illuminates the world,
Putting a smile on every face.
This is me...

A mbitious
A rdent
R adiant
A chiever
V ibrant like the sun forever, glistening like a huge gold coin.

Aarav Chakraverty (10)

This Is Me

I am *green*,
I am keen,
I am sometimes sad,
But it is not that *bad*,
There are times when people *freeze*,
But I am like a tree in a breeze,
Sometimes I hear a voice to stop who I am,
But that does no matter to me,
One day, when I grow up,
I will *change* the world to make it better,
I will write a powerful speech,
I will go to the right path,
No one will stop *me*,
I do not care if I am different,
I will just seek the future...

Sehansa De Silva (9)

My Birthday

Waking up enthusiastic, I feel I'm *going to burst*,
My birthday, what a wonderful thing,
All a smile makes my happiness disperse,
Now I get some presents, I feel like a king,
Thinking about all the sweet cake,
Going to a birthday play date and party,
Eating the cake that someone will make,
When at the party, welcoming hearty,
Games played, enjoyable,
Food, amazing, yummy,
Cake is delicious and eatable,
Everything wrapped by my mummy,
See all my friends next year!

Kunarathan Parameswaran (9)

Fear

F ailing isn't an option, competing takes a lot of courage, it's a concoction of feelings swirling around.

E veryone is staring at you, I am thankful I am with my dance crew, however, when you are up there alone, you secretly wish you are at home. It's like butterflies fluttering around in my stomach.

A drenaline kicks in as soon as the music starts, the fear disappears; this is the best part!

R elief... It's over! This is the moment I feel proud, I have conquered the fear!

Lexie-Jae Lomax (10)

What Do I Want To Be?

What to be, what to be,
What do I want to be?
I'm braver and stronger,
I could be a runner,
I'm older and smarter,
I could be a doctor,
I might go down the right paths,
Although I'm not too great at maths,
I love to read and write,
It makes me feel bright,
I have brown long hair,
It flows behind me in the air,
My favourite colour is blue,
But I like green too,
So what should I really be,
What do I want to be?
In time, we'll see...

Evie Sadler (11)

In Your Eyes

In your eyes, I see frustration
In your eyes, I see beauty
In your eyes, I see contact
I look deeper,
In your eyes, I can see strength
In your eyes, I can see determination
In your eyes, I can see power

In your heart, I can see kindness
In your heart, I can see pureness
In your heart, I can see fear
I focus,
In your heart, I can see concentration
In your heart, I can see love
In your heart, I can see patience

In your body and soul, I see you.

Felicity Rogers (9)

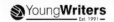

Lottie In A Nut Shell

I like to sing,
I like to dance,
I like to write things in verse,

I have a thing for stories,
Adventures,
Mystery,
Just not gories,

I have a cat that likes to purr,
I have a tortoise that is a her,
My gerbils are very cute,
My parents are much more astute,

My house is old,
But very bold,
My allotment is sweet,
And we grow beet,

This is the end of the poem,
But not the end of me,
I have so many things left to see.

Charlotte Ruby Karger (11)

Love

Love visited me.
They flew through the door,
They said they were here,
To throw a party.

They had cakes and cookies,
As precious as gold.
The boys wore red and black,
And the girls wore pink and gold.

They had brown eyes and long smiles.
They asked for a drink of beer and I said yes,
I had the best of the rest,
So I put it to the test and I saw a bird's nest.

They said goodbye after we ate and drank,
they flew,
As the wind blew.

Kwame Baillie (8)

This Girl Is Different

Joyful
Beaming brightly
When it all goes smoothly
Shining sparks of wonder appear
Fun times

Anger
When it goes wrong
The blood keeps boiling
Fierce smoke is bursting everywhere
Temper

Happy
Determined mind
Challenges are nice things
Being hard on yourself is bad
Dig deep

Fury
Rage and anger
A temper makes its rise
If something has not gone alright
Calm down

Funny
Laughing loudly
Any joke that is said
A mischievous grin appears
Cheeky

I am proud of who I am
Embrace your difference
Unique
Brave
Strong
It's you.

Lara Almashta (10)

This Is My Life

My name is Azalea
My friends call me funny
I only have two BFFs
One of them has a pet bunny

I love to go to school
I like to read a book
I read thirty minutes a day
My friends have good luck

I love to spend time in nature
Love to see precious animals
I like to see cats, but I'm allergic to them
My favourite animal is a camel

Animals are precious
I like to see dogs
Once, I kept tadpoles
And they turned into frogs.

Azalea Ward (8)

I Am...

A mazing at cricket, Lego construction too
B uilder of magnificent Minecraft houses
H appy watching television on the sofa
A ctive, agile swimmer and footballer too
Y es, this is me

K ind and knowledgeable about cars
H aving fun playing fantastic games with parents
A ffectionate to my grandparents in India
N aughty but not notorious
N ever ever say no to Haribo
A bhay Khanna is the name.

Abhay Khanna (9)

My Perfect Day

I opened the stable door at dawn
And was greeted by my pony's yawn
After a bit of mucking out
I saddled up and began to mount
We started with a gentle trot
I gave a squeeze, we sped up a lot
As we galloped into the sun
Me and my pony were having so much fun!
I rode for as long as I was able
Then we headed back to the stable
When sunset began to loom
I gave my pony a thorough groom
As he lay down in the hay
I knew we'd had the perfect day!

Daisy-Mae Gaunt (10)

Skateboard

S kateboarding is my favourite activity.
K arate is about defending myself.
A lcohol is not good for my age.
T eam spirit is very important in a group.
E lectronic devices make me addicted sometimes.
B rothers are my best friends in my life.
O ccasionally I have nosebleeds.
A ndrea is after my grandad's name.
R iddle poems got me into writing.
D elightful mindset keeps me a happy boy.

Andrea Fuorvito (7)

This Is Me - Pavaki Singh

My name is Pavaki Singh
My favourite season is spring
I don't like the fruit peach
But I love going to the beach
I don't find it fun
Going for a run
I like doing lots of art
Especially drawing a love heart
My favourite colour is pink
When I go swimming, I try not to sink
It's fun watching television
But what to watch is a hard decision
I love mac 'n' cheese
But not with mushy peas
When I go to sleep
I usually count some sheep
Goodbye, everyone
I hope you had fun!

Pavaki Singh (8)

The Luckiest Person In The World

For me, I feel like the luckiest person in the world.
First of all, I have a loving family.
I was born in the UK,
But I am from Uganda, Tanzania and Kenya.
My grandfather is John Maumo.
I have an uncle who has five hotels.
My dad is a businessman.
So I live in a rich family,
But I don't take advantage of that.
I have a loving family.
I am a nice, gentle person,
And I write poems for me,
Because it makes me feel calm.

Elizabeth Wamalwa (12)

My Dream

Up, up high, up, up high,
Flying in the sky.

Going up high,
Supersonic in the NASA spaceship.

Discover new planets,
New galaxies.
Let the dream come true...

Have a breakfast on the moon.
Have a packet of macaroons.
Reach home soon.

Fish for the stars in a bowl.
Come back by Christmas and
Travel through a wormhole.

Discover new planets,
New galaxies.
Let the dream come true...

Aarya Dubey (7)

Spy

Eyes, my eyes gaze upon the sun whilst the trees
spy on me.
Dancing birds in the trees, playing delightfully.
Sometimes they spy on me.
Wind blows through the trees.
Branches bend down, are they still trying to spy on
me?
As the trees and birds spy on me,
I trip into the shadows of the trees, still spying
on me.
Running fast to get away from them so they stop
spying on me.
Dad helps me hide so they can no longer spy
on me.

Edward Farr (9)

Unique (What Am I?)

Beautiful
A spectacle to behold
Colours of rage and sorrow
Illuminate the sky
Led by joy and excitement
Sparkles trail in the night
Like memories
At least until they fade
What an experience
Second to none
As the actions reflect in the blue sea
The light will always linger
Up till you never hope
God's best creation yet
Its supremacy cannot be bested
For it's one of a kind
But many...

Harijeeth Reddy Parvatha

The Pleasure Of Books

Some books are happy
Some books are sad
Some are long
Some are mad

Books are your friend
Books are here till the end
Books can help you mend
To a magical place they send

Books are like a different world
The real and the magical all get swirled
Books take you to different lands
To blue bays and golden sands

So pick up a book
Find a nook
Dive in
Let the magic begin!

Sienna Scarff (8)

This Is Me

My name is Evie,
If you didn't know.
I'm eleven years old,
And still continue to grow.

I like sports,
As they help clear my mind.
Art is relaxing to do,
Every drawing is one of a kind.

I'm awfully fond of reading,
Mysteries and adventures are favourites of mine.
Though I do love all sorts of stories,
Non-fiction books are fine.

So, this is me,
I'm probably not at all like you.
We are all different, you see,
Be different and stand tall.

Evie Corcoran (11)

It's Me!

A nightingale of my family, lookalike of my dad but it is me!

M ay it rain or snow, I am out in the park, exploring the nature and playing with my toys.

A dventurous, creative and a cheerful little light.

E ager to become a horse rider and as flexible as gymnast as an adult.

Y ou inspire me as a lovely and a kind teacher.

A s beautiful and adorable as a cute flamingo, a brave firefighter, a sweet and sour candy is me!

Amaeya Iyengar (7)

Welcome To My Little Bubble

K atelyn is my name
A n actress I will be
T aking videos for all to see.
E lephants are my favourite
L ollipop, I savour it.
Y o-yos I pay with
N ever-ending are my stories

S uperhero or villain?
T hat Harley Quinn is my idol.
O bsessed with reading
N ow I'm exploring The Midnight Gang
E llie is my favourite teddy.

Katelyn Stone (9)

All About Me

My name is Aadam Hussain,
I love my family, especially my brother Zayn.

I love to eat pizza and chocolate cake,
And play with my cars and dinosaurs when I'm awake.

My favourite all-time word has to be 'no',
As I know it keeps my mum on her toes.

My favourite programmes are Sonic and Ninja Kids TV,
Which my older sister likes to sit and watch with me.

If I like you, I'll give you a smile,
But please be warned, it may take a while!

Aadam Hussain (3)

I Am...

I am the creative girl who wrote this poem and
loves art.
I don't care what anyone says about me or the
things I do,
I'm a strong girl.

I'm independent and intelligent,
No one can stop me.
I wear my heart on my sleeve for anyone who
needs it.

Everyone says I'm fun and my energy,
Is always high.

I'm working hard for the armed forces.
I'm passionate and believe,
I can achieve what I want to,
If I put my mind to it.

Isabelle Robinson (10)

I Wish

I wish I could be a rushing river
racing with the land

I wish I could be a whirling wind
praising the rising sun

I wish I could be a tall tree
standing in front of the soaring sky

I wish I could be a beautiful bird
that glides gracefully

I wish I could be a lightning lamp
to lit the demon's darkness

I wish I could be a happy heart
protecting a precious person's body

I wish I could be an ink
illustrating on my parchment paper.

Saswath Govindasamy Raja (7)

Construction Instructions

Do you want to know,
How to create me?
Well then. You need a...
Sloth lover,
Keen reader,
Eager writer,
Dancer-in-training,
Obsessive swimmer,
Singing fanatic,
Harry Potter superfan,
Music writer (sometimes!),
Music player (when I want to!),
Girl Guide,
Sileby local,
Left-hander,
Glasses wearer,
Hemiplegia born,
Brown hair and blue eyes,
Nature enthusiast.
And to cap it all off:

I'm in Hufflepuff!
And there you have me!

Poppy Halsall (11)

This Is Me

I like to celebrate what I do,
Who I am and what I like too
I never forget the people I know,
For they are the ones who have helped me to grow
They make me feel glad that I'm here,
That I am safe and have nothing to fear
People love me wherever I go,
I know this because they say so
So when somebody says,
"I don't like you,"
I reply to them,
"Well, I do."

Greta Winkelgrund (10)

This Is Who I Am Meant To Be

I'm not full of beauty
But you can see the beauty in my eyes
My eyes look like earth growing
My eyes make me special
My hair is covered in brown with hidden blondes
I'm not that good at maths
I focus my colours in art
I take care of the people who need it more
I'm kind
I'm helpful
I'm joyful
I'm friendly
This is me and I'm meant to be this person.

Miley Colbourne (7)

Corey

C urious, courageous, crazy, and cute, can be very annoying sometimes

O reos are one of my favourite snacks, over-dramatic at times, over the moon when I score a goal for any football team

R unning is something I'm really good at, rarely not playing football

E nergetic when it comes to sports, eager to please my family

Y um-yums are my favourite food in the world, yummy mummy.

Corey Wilton (10)

Muhammad Ayaan's Recipe Book

Ingredients:

My recipe book
One large smile
One cup of respect
Half a cup of sharing
A pinch of humour
Teaspoon of confidence
Tablespoon of shyness

Method:

Mix me together
Pour me in a bowl
Serve me whole
Feel my warmth
Taste my sweetness
Smell my completeness
Share me, take care of me
A recipe full of Muhammad Ayaan
Enjoy!

Muhammad Ayaan Mehmood (9)

This Is Me

I love money, I'm not funny
My feelings can't break like bone, stone
I love writing
My besties always moan

I love my animals
I have the ability to see
We have trees for oxygen
I can be a bee in a tree

I hate hurting animals
I hate jeans
I hate directions
I hate beans

I love electricity
I love food
I love fights
I'm in a mood.

Laila Gregory

Christmas Day

Christmas Day, what a winter day.
Snow sprinkling down all the way.
Angels, baubles, and decorations hung on the tree.
Hums of joy, will there be for thee?
Christmas crackers are being pulled apart.
Carols that fill everyone's heart.
Cracking jokes and colossal crowns.
Turkey and gravy.
Carrots and peas.
And finally, the gifts from Santa arrive.
They open their gifts with great surprise.
In the cosy and warm winter night.

Vishnusri Priya Mendu (11)

Josiah

Hi, my name is Josiah and I like to rap.
I like playing video games too,
Those are one of my favourite subjects that I love doing.
My favourite video game is Fortnite.
I play it every Friday, Saturday, and Sunday.
My favourite rapper is Digga D and he inspired me.
That is why I like to rap.
God will give me strength and braveness.
I will have a good future and God will give me courage.

Josiah Campbell (10)

'Cause That's My Thing!

I love to play and dance and sing
May you ask why?
'Cause that's my thing!

In hockey, my stick I love to swing
May you ask why?
'Cause that's my thing!

I love to flip and turn and spring
May you ask why?
'Cause that's my thing!

In netball, the ball I love to fling
May you ask why?
'Cause that's my thing!

I love to play football on the wing
May you ask why?
'Cause that's my thing!

Emilia Salter (9)

I Am Amy

A miable, I'm always a friend
M ature, I'm quite grown up
Y ummy, I love most food

F antastic friend to people who know me
R eally happy person most of the time!
E nergetic, I'm always on the go
E ager to learn
M any think I'm funny
A rtistic, mostly found with a pen or pencil
N oisy and loud.

Amy Freeman (8)

This Is Me

I'm as happy as a boy can be,
I have a brother and he is three.

I'm a lightning bolt in football boots,
As I run, tackle, jump and powerfully shoot.

All the healthy food I eat,
From crunchy carrots to marvellous meat.

I love my parents lots and lots,
And I'm grateful for all the things I've got.

As I'm sure you can tell and I'm sure you can see,
All the things in this poem are all about me.

Theo Calafatis (8)

Awesome

To be awesome, you have to be daring,
And I don't mean scaring,
You have to stand up to things and never back
down, or you'll drown,
Listen to people and they will listen to you,
That way, you will find your new soul,
Be humble, so you can bumble like a bee and be
free,
Never grumble and moan,
Or you will turn to stone,
Always be supportive, so no one has to be let
down,
If only I could find someone like you.

Fiona Olubori (10)

Football

F ootball is my favourite sport

O n the field, I'm always running.

O ff the field, I like to draw.

T he thing I like about football is you make friends

B all skills is my favourite focus.

A ll the people on the pitch have different positions.

L earning is how everyone gets better.

L osing can teach me how to be better and faster.

Isla Aharon (8)

Henry The Amazing Cowboy

I have eyes as blue as sapphires
I have freckles on my nose
I am strong and I am kind
I have ten tickly toes
I love to watch Harry Potter
I like to make my own spells
I shout, "Expelliarmus!"
I want to be famous and stay in hotels.
I play with Bruder tractors
Lambykins is my favourite toy
I take my lamb to the stables
I am Henry the amazing cowboy!

Henry Gee (8)

About Me

When I grow up, I want to be a person who does nails and makes people happy.
And with that, I need God on my side.
Then when He is with me, I have the strength to carry on.
And make my dream come to life.
Maybe I won't get there, I know I won't get there yet.
But God is my friend and there's nothing you can do without God.
I want to be what I want to be.
This is me!

Jedelyn Campos Aragon

My Favourite Animal

I am a great ball of fur
And a ray of sunshine
I like eating leaves
People mistake me for a bear
I have a big black nose
And big furry ears
I like to climb trees
And play with my pals
I am as small as a bunny
And as cute as a teddy bear
I only live in one place
And this one place is very hot
What am I?

Answer: A koala.

Sasha McGlynn

I'm Me

I'm not squeamish, I rarely
Scare.
I hardly cry, but not because
I'm apathetic or don't care.
I just express myself differently,
Through poetry or the emotions I share.
That's not a crime, not here,
Not anywhere.
Some people show who they are
From their flair or what
They wear,
But I'm me and that's how
It should be; fair.

Joanna Luncan (11)

Spring

Starting spring is always fun
Glitz and glam for everyone
Critters wake up from their hibernation
As the southern birds come to sing
Love spreads from thing to thing
As the buds and blossom start to thrive
Spring becomes very divine
As the seedlings and flowers are planted
Everybody's wishes are granted
As sheep give birth to lambs
Nature becomes glam.

Radhika Satish

Succeed

I am me, I am the air that I breathe
No one can knock me down
For they will end up
With a frown
I won't give up
I will never stop
Till I reach the top
The world needs kids
Like me
Otherwise, it will
Fall to its knees
The Earth has rights
For you, we will fight
And raise the light
I am sure you agree
It is time to be free.

Zahra Anis (10)

Find My Own Way

This is me
I am strong
I am brave
I know I am the key
For me

I let the negatives take control
And it brings down my soul
So I will fight
For what is right

I am kind
I am not blind
To the world around me
This is me

I let the negatives take control
And it brings down my soul
So I will fight
For what is right

I am bright
I am confident
And I know what is right

This is me.

Islah Malik (10)

Welcome To My World

A human with big hopes and dreams!
Adventure books and games in-between!
A myriad of sports that makes your adrenaline pump!
Basketball, badminton and dodgeball all tangled together as I jump!
I like to read books and enter new worlds!
I can be funny, caring, sometimes a little puzzled!
My world of adventure, inspiration, imagination and bravery will not be smashed to smithereens!
Because I am me!

Laraib Malik (11)

About Me!

I like books.
My dad cooks.
And when someone makes fun of me.
I consider them a crook!

When I am sad.
My parents make me glad.
And when I am feeling gloom.
They make my happy expressions bloom.

Splash!
I like going to swimming pools.
It's like when I dive in, I feel like I look cool!
I am as gentle as an angel.
People say, and that makes my cheerful smile
come out as I fly away!

Jesziah Atan

Rocket Moon

I see balls of fire in night-time sky,
It is time to say goodbye,
To this world I will fold
And will put in my pocket
A crafted paper rocket
That will fly me to the moon!

The moon is so delightful,
But the holes are so frightful,
My house up there is wonderful,
But just imagine living there,
It would be more amazing than anywhere.

Noah Flavelle (10)

Happy

The happiest feeling going around,
Makes you laugh and giggle, like you've found,
A piece of treasure in the sea,
Now just look and you can be,

Anything you want,
Come and look,
You can even write a book,

The joy inside you makes you proud,
With a touch of love,
And a bit of a cloud,

Now time to rest,
The feeling goes away,
Don't be sad,
It will come back another day.

Maiya Sandberg (7)

Me, The Maple Tree

M arvellous, magical, friendly and playful, I have a lot to make my day full.

A rty, careful, loving and kind, amazing thoughts go through my mind.

P leasant, lovely, animal-lover, likes to get on with one another

L ovely, caring, bright and bubbly, cute am I and oh so cuddly.

E asy-going, fun and free, this is me the maple tree.

Maple Doherty (14)

Who Am I?

My Welsh identity is important to me,
I like to go to the beach and it's the place to be,
All the things I do are important to me,
I love to do colouring, it's just me,
I like playing schools with my brother,
I like to play Barbies with my mummy and have
bath bombs too,
I like to scare my brother by saying boo,
I like my mummy and daddy,
I like my life,
Don't you?

Elizabeth Edwards (7)

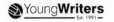

I Am Who I Want To Be

This is me, I am who I want to be
I don't mind if people say bad things about me
People may describe me as strong-willed
But I can use that for my leadership skills
My hobbies are baking, swimming, art and LAMDA
I love my hobbies
I know that I am good at them
I'm from Nigeria and I am proud of my black skin
When I am doing a good thing, I will never give up.

Amenaghawon Olaye (9)

Minecraft

M ighty player, like an Avenger

I ncredibly good at Minecraft

N ight-time, it's dangerous at night-time in Minecraft

E xtreme at Minecraft

C rafting master

R acing around like a hamster on a wheel

A ll the time on my game

F ast and furious

T ill we beat the Ender Dragon.

Thomas Keenan (7)

This Is Me

T he master of all art.
H elpful when it comes to improving.
I can dance to any music.
S ing sweet songs to myself.

I can create a wave of laughter within seconds.
S wift and silent in school, loud and nutty outside.

M y friends make me stronger.
E nemies, I have none.

Madison Ward (10)

This Is Me

My name is Samson.
Samson means incredible strength.
Just like my name, I am strong and fun.
Samson also means the sun.
I shine bright and I am full of energy.
I give off orange and yellow rays of calm and happiness.
If you need cheering up, I'll brighten up your day.
If you need any help, I'll be sure to show you the way.

Samson Cohen (7)

All About Me!

J asmine, me, has brown hair

A nimals are my favourite thing because they are wild

S hining eyes that are so bright

M agnificent at art because it is my favourite thing to do

I am kind because I help

N ice because I help tidy up

E nergetic at running as it is my favourite thing to do outside.

Jasmine Patel (7)

Me

I love nature, which dances in the wind
And says to me
Be yourself
Nature's leaves frozen into ice
Makes shapes that are very nice
Lakes are so peaceful
But ducks quack loud
I love nature

I love books
Read three per day
I love books
That is what I say
A different story in each one
Is how I know I am done
Every book has magic
Not doom and tragic
I love books!

Daphne Erkut (8)

Lockdown

L ockdown was boring

O ften we had to stay at home, we had a holiday

C an't see my family nor my friends

K eeping everyone at home except animals

D own is sad like, up is good

O ceans were quiet with calmness

W e were at home for a very long time

N ow we need a big smile!

Anamta Abrar (9)

I Am So Many Things

I am a super striker, dribbling past defenders
I am a rapper, better than Stormzy
I am as brave as a lion, as cheeky as a monkey
I am as determined as an ox, as sneaky as a fox
I am as kind as a nurse, as gentle as a mouse
I am courageous and fearless, and nothing can
stop me
I am a captain, leading others on
This is me.

Oma Olaye (11)

This Is Me

This is me,
I'm happy when I'm dancing
I'm happy when I'm acting
I'm happy when I'm singing as well as when I'm reading.

I love to cook
I love to bake
I love to write from day to day

I love my pets
I love my friends
I love my warm and comfy bed

Goodnight...

Abigail Miller (9)

An Acrostic Nathaniel Poem

N ow it's time to learn about me!

A n example of me is dragons, but

T hat is only one thing about me.

H ow do I tell you?

A ll I can tell you is for

N ow I love Lego and card games with

I magination because they're more fun.

E verything is possible, like

L ego designing - my dream.

Nathaniel Rose (9)

In The City

I love the city!
N ight and day!

T oday is busy.
H ouse of Parliament was built in 1860.
E lephants don't live here.

C ars drive around on the roads.
I t is buzzing with people.
T raffic jams are spread all over London.
Y esterday is exactly the same as today!

Anna Legg (7)

That's Okay

Sometimes I get mad
And sometimes I get sad
And that's okay
Sometimes I get tired
And really uninspired
And that's okay
Sometimes I get snappy
But...
I can be really, really happy
I can be excited... and delighted
So now you know, I can be
Mad, sad, tired, uninspired, snappy, happy, excited
and delighted
... and that's okay.

Isabelle Freya George (10)

I Am Friendly

F ood is my favourite thing.
R adishes are red, round and yummy.
I dentical twins are still unique.
E very day I make a new friend.
N etball is a fun sport.
D omenico is my dad's name.
L aura is my name.
Y esterday, I ate a burger.

Laura Figoli (8)

Never Eat Pineapple On Pizza!

If you have pineapple on pizza, you are so weird.
It should be illegal to put pineapple on pizza.
I can barely say 'pineapple on pizza'
Without getting weirded out.
Pineapple on pizza is disgusting.
Pineapple on pizza is as disgusting as hippo poo!
Never eat pineapple on pizza!

Skylar Mansell

The Wonderful World Of Me!

In the wonderful world of me,
Clocks tick quick,
Rats play with cats,
Books make looks,
Art makes hearts.

In the wonderful world of me,
Rainbows flow to create rivers,
Kitties are pretty,
Llamas are loving,
Dragons are lions,
All of this just happens to be in the wonderful
world of me,
Where anything is possible.

Lola Crossley (10)

This Is Me

A ll about me means everything about me
S iyona, Idhika, Yashica and Shyla are my friends
H eaven will know we will be
V ery gorgeous friends
I love dancing, singing and swimming
K nowledge and kindness are my traits
A nd I just wanted to ask you

Was this poem thrilling?

Ashvika Shenoy (8)

Nabeeha

My name is Nabeeha,
I am someone no one else can be,
I am glad to be me,
I am scared of bees,
I always flee,
I am as tall as a tree,
I have dreams that take me out to sea,
I like to play with my cousin of three,
I am the best I can be,
That's the story of me.

Nabeeha Khandaker (10)

Summer

S ummer is when I visit my grandparents

U mbrellas on the beach to give me shade from the sun

M ango and strawberry ice creams, my favourite

M ussels are fresh and yummy during summer

E ating ice lollies all day long

R iding my bike to the beach.

Sara Figoli (8)

This Is Me

N ancy is my name and this is who I am
A rt is my favourite subject because it's lots of fun
N ow and forever I will do my best
C lothes keep me warm because I wear my vest
Y ou are you and I am me - different but let's live
in harmony.

Nancy Harris (8)

Any Time, Any Goal

I had a goal to win one day
But I played all day.
I didn't win because I didn't try my best.
What a shame!
But I believed one day I would win
So I had to stay and complete my goal.
I did it the next day
So I'll have to make a harder goal one day.

Mason Wright (10)

This Is Me

My favourite thing is art,
I love that part.
I enjoy drinking juicy drinks
I love my mom, she is so cute.
I enjoy going out and
I love to swim with a splash, splash, splosh
I love my cat
And he loves a pat.
I love the sound of rain
With no pain.

Alishba Latif (11)

My Dream

M y dream, my dream
Y ou could have a dream just like me

D reaming of writing a best-selling book
R eading and reading to get inspiration
E veryone will love my book
A nyone can read it
M y dream, my dream.

Indie Dawber (8)

Isobel

I am Isobel,

S ometimes I drink some Fanta,

O verjoyed at Christmas and birthdays I am,

B elieving in unicorns is essential,

E velyn is the best sister ever!

L oving my kind family is my favourite part about me!

Isobel Crowther (10)

This Is Me

T here is nobody like me,
"H orn the born, Mum!"
I s this me speaking?
S eeing my nanna today,

I love her so, so, so much,
S leep, sleep, I'm going to sleep.

M adison is my name,
E ight is my number.

Madison Reddaway (8)

About Me, Kenning Poetry

Starry name
Poet became
Only child
Cat's wild
Sensible, sharing
Always caring
Kindness river
Happiness giver
Monkey mad
Pink's bad
Food fan
Mushroom ban
Art maker
Walk taker
French learner
Medal earner
Game player
Mob slayer
Tap dancer
Life enhancer.

Seren Campbell (9)

This Is Me

I like prawns and Toblerone,
They aren't a good mix.
I love Marvel and Lego,
Which is a good mix.
My family means the world to me
And the world's a good place,
With a bit more helpfulness,
It can be a better place.

Avi Patel (9)

Harmony

I love to sing and it brings me joy
I love my brother like a toy
Sometimes he is annoying, but he is so cute
You should see me sing, and my brother can
sing along
Don't forget I am a song
I bring world peace and harmony.

Harmony Tendo (9)

Like A Reindeer

Dancing makes me feel like a reindeer,
Leaping through the woods I go,
Strong and steady, energy ready,
Gold is the colour I feel today,
Leaping and spinning away,
Joyful, I will be,
Feeling like a reindeer, free.

Sophie Wilson

This Is Me

I am a mischievous monkey
Swinging from branch to branch
I am a flexible friend
With you until the end
I am as cool as a cucumber
My hair is as flat as a pancake
My teeth look like chipmunks'
This is me.

Georgi

It's Me!

I love music
I love a crisp
I love sleeping
I'm always dreaming
I sing a song
My mum joins along
I hate being sick
The clock never ticks
I'll be a poet
Because this is
Me!

Syeda Hamnah Shah (10)

I Am Oliver

I am Oliver.

The creator of comics,
The lover of pasta,
The player of games.

The jumbler of spellings,
The tumbler of toys,
The misplacer of things.

The scribbler of notebooks,
The muncher of biscuits,
The creator of art.

This is me.

Oliver Tabita (10)

This Is Me

T en years of age I am
H elpful as I can be
O n top of the world with
M y friends
A ll my friends say I am polite and kind
S upportive and strong, the best friend you can have.

Thomas Manns-Moran

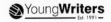

This Is Me

J acket keeps me warm every day.

E nergetically, I jump on my trampoline.

N aughty brothers of mine make me get in trouble.

N ow, I'm eight years old.

A tablet of mine is broken.

Jenna Islam (8)

Me, The Nine-Year Nerd As Called

Nine years old
Can't be controlled
I'm quite small
Sometimes, I bawl
My hair is definitely a mess
I really like chess
I always win, more or less
I look like a nerd
But that is absurd
I really like steak
And the summer break!

Ziad Abdelnaby (9)

This Is Me

I like dogs and cats,
I like to play on colourful mats.
I like maths and English,
I love to be distinguished.
I like school,
And I like pools,
The flowers brightly bloom,
And my ancestors used a loom.
This is me, and I am free.

Alveen Muhammad

All About Me

I am a ray of sunshine,
Peeking through the curtains.
I am a crackling firework,
Rising up to the place up high.
And even though times are tough,
I can still zoom up and fly!
Flapping my imaginary wings,
Soaring across the sky!

Shreya Bhardwaj (11)

My Dog Is Called Nelly

I have a dog called Nelly,
And she looks like a belly.
She has a friend called Shelly,
And he looks like a furry belly.
Nelly is a piece of my heart,
And she loves to fart,
And it makes me laugh.

Nanaki Sandhu (9)

Happy, Helpful Harley

H amsters are cute
A mazing at art
R eally can't stop biting my nails
L ong, lovely highlighted hair
E xcellent at reading
Y oung Harley wants to be a YouTuber!

Harley Haldane (9)

Unapologetically Me!

U ltra-energetic!
N ot following the crowd!
I nspiration to my baby brother.
Q uirky fashion sense.
U nderstanding of others and their differences.
E xceptional heart.

Ophelia Morgan-Dew (7)

School Of The Future

I'm gonna build an aeroplane,
With a school on the bottom
And four other bungalows
For pets in need,
Because I want to be kind to
Humans and pets,
So this is me in the future.

Harley Vahabzadeh (8)

This Is Me!

I am happy Alexandra.
Happy like the rainbow.
Grey are my eyes, brown is my hair colour.
I am nine years old, in Year 4.
Pink is my personality and I've got a hamster as
white as snow.

Alexandra Dankowska (9)

This Is Me

I am as smart as a chimpanzee.
I am as tall as a giraffe.
I am as fast as a cheetah.
I have sharp eyesight like an eagle.
All these animals are just like me, lots of animals
are like me!
This is me!

Sukeeth Venkiteela (7)

All About Me!

I am a football super striker,
I am as fast as a bullet,
I am as active as a kangaroo,
I jump so high it looks like I'm on a trampoline,
I am as kind and loving as God.

Ólan Tracey

Chloe's Acrostic Poem

C are for others.

H elp people in trouble.

L ove your family and friends.

O thers' opinions matter.

E nough kindness to go around!

Chloe Thorley (8)

This Is Me

The best sport is football
I am the fastest of all;
I train every Wednesday
I love it when my friends play
I love it when we win.
Just come and see my grin.

Teddy Mitchel (7)

This Is Me!

A kennings poem

I am a...
Curry eater
Family meeter
Football player
Music listener
Hilarious joker
Mushroom hater
Friend maker
Goosebumps reader.

Dillon Smith (11)

What Is It?

You have to learn it,
It's in the water,
You have to wear special gear.
You can do it anywhere in water,
Your body gets wet,
You can splash it,

What is it?

Maya Leeming (9)

Happy Day

Today is going to be bright
Like the sunlight
You will feel unique
In just a tick
You will be tired
At the end of the day
And all your worries
Will go away!

Devna Sanal

Learn About Me And My Lifestyle

J ess likes jaguars
E xcited about her future in life
S acks full of laughter
S pooks of Halloween.

Jessica Manns-Moran

Mahder

M arvellous

A mazing

H eroic

D elightful

E legant

R espectful.

Mahder Yohanes

Things About Me

A kennings poem

Sweet treat eater
Amazing adventurer
Agile runner
Great climber
Comic reader
TV watcher
Game player
Great listener.

Edwyn Rhys-Davies (7)

 YoungWriters® Est. 1991

YOUNG WRITERS INFORMATION

We hope you have enjoyed reading this book – and that you will continue to in the coming years.

If you're the parent or family member of an enthusiastic poet or story writer, do visit our website **www.youngwriters.co.uk/subscribe** and sign up to receive news, competitions, writing challenges and tips, activities and much, much more! There's lots to keep budding writers motivated!

If you would like to order further copies of this book, or any of our other titles, then please give us a call or order via your online account.

Young Writers
Remus House
Coltsfoot Drive
Peterborough
PE2 9BF
(01733) 890066
info@youngwriters.co.uk

Join in the conversation!
Tips, news, giveaways and much more!

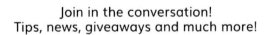

 **YoungWritersUK**  **YoungWritersCW** 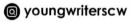 **youngwriterscw**